Revolution™

LEANER HEALTHIER TEENS

"LHT's, live a leaner longer life!" ™

by Cynthia Besson

Library of Congress Control Number: 2012940509

ISBN 978-0-615-6250-1

Printed in the United States of America

M Com Publishing soft-cover edition July 2012
For more information about special discounts for bulk purchases, please contact
M Com Publishing at 916.939.3344 or log onto our website at: www.mcompublishing.com

Design by Lisa Baraya and Sam Sellers

Editing by Illana Burke

Photography by Gail Shoop Lamy

Table of Contents

Acknowledgements

This book is dedicated to my sister Sandy, and my mother Judy, who I lost to type 2 Diabetes. I wrote and created this program in hopes of saving other families from this unnecessary tragedy.

Thanks to all the teens that helped me create this successful program including Felicia, Kaitlin, Adrienne, Rachel, Laura, Erin, Matt, Keith, Priya, Kathleen, Arjun, Madison, Nick, Parkyre, Sierra and Alex. **Thanks for helping to change lives, by having the courage to change your own!**

A special thanks to Kyrsta, my teen administrative assistant for all your hard work. Much love and appreciation go to my good friends Jimmy, Chelsea, Kebra, Lisa, Kat, Lori and Tammy for putting up with me while creating this and never allowing me to give up on it.

I am blessed to have such good friends in my life.

Thank you also to my family, my Aunt, Uncle, Father and Sister Shelly for your kind words of encouragement and belief in me. You may not know it or believe it, but I did hear every word you said!

Special acknowledgments to all our licensees both current and future, who are helping take up this cause and become part of our team. The people I have met, (and whom I have yet to meet,) are talented, educated, committed and passionate about changing this epidemic. One of my favorite quotes is by Mohamed Gandhi which states, "If we could change ourselves, the tendencies in the world would also change. As a person changes their own nature, so does the attitude of the world change towards them. We need not wait to see what others do." In other words.... be the change you wish to see!" These caring individuals are doing just that. I thank them in advance, from the bottom of my heart, for trusting the LHT program enough to not only pick up this book, but to *put it into action* in their communities. YOU, my friends, partners, team mates, will be the reason for increasing a child's health and self-esteem, not to mention their lifespan!

"Never doubt that a small group of thoughtful committed citizens can change the world—indeed, it is the only thing that ever does."

- Margaret Meade

Forward

We can hardly pick up the newspaper, turn on the television or drive by a school without noticing that obesity is on the rise across our country, not only in adults but in our youth as well. However, it seems that very few parents understand the ramifications of one in three of our teens being overweight. In 1970, only five percent of teens were overweight and today we are at almost triple that percentage. This phenomenon is happening worldwide. In the United States children of African American, Hispanic and Native-American descent, as well as those from low income families are most susceptible to weight gain. According to the 1999-2000 NHANES (**National Health and Nutrition Examination Survey**) study, fifteen percent of Caucasians, twenty-three percent of Mexican-Americans, and twenty-four percent of African Americans, between the ages of eleven and nineteen, were overweight. The same study indicated that younger children age six to eleven were only slightly less overweight than teens. Overweight children are at risk for all kinds of grown up diseases including hypertension, high cholesterol, insulin resistance, obstructive sleep apnea, metabolic syndrome, asthma and diabetes.

"Childhood diabetes is approaching catastrophic proportions."
- American Diabetes Association

What is happening here? Why are we as adults letting this happen to our children? I believe if we are to save a lost generation from obesity, we need to start now, and the Leaner, Healthier Teen Revolution (LHTR) program is doing just that. Thankfully, LHTR is stepping up to help fight this epidemic using unique tools like social media, interactive classroom teaching sessions, webinars, and community outreach programs to connect with our youth.

"60 percent of overweight children have at least one cardiovascular disease risk."
- National Institute of Child Health and Human Development

This book is perfectly timed and I whole-heartedly feel that the LHTR program will spread like wildfire. There is obviously a huge demand and need for the transformational, educational experience that lies between these pages. The LHTR program stands above the rest because it addresses the physical, emotional and behavioral aspects of making healthy eating choices. It's not a diet and exercise program; it's a lifestyle program. It requires that the LHTR students learn to listen to their bodies and their emotions and develop the ability to be mindful and self-reflective. The mindfulness approach works because our greatest growth and change occurs when we become more self-aware. We must teach our youth to be kind and to love themselves, no matter what they weigh and the LHTR program does that brilliantly.

"One in three children born in the year 2000 will develop diabetes at some point in his or her lifetime."
- Center for Disease Control and Prevention

"61 percent of girls and 28 percent of boys have dieted to lose weight in the last year. 27 percent of girls and 12 percent of boys vomit to lose weight, 11 percent use diet pills and 7 percent diet more than 10 times a year!"
- Cleveland State University Study

As an educational curriculum designer, the LHTR program is well designed to create lasting, healthy life style changes. The lessons in this book empower young adults by addressing the cognitive, behavioral and emotional aspects of making healthy eating choices. They haven't left one stone unturned! The classes make it not only an educational process, but a fun and safe learning environment for our children.

Kimberly Walker, Ph.D.
Health Education

Focusing on youth obesity, LHT addresses America's biggest health problem "head on". Written for the teen as a planner, a reference and a journal, Cynthia has created a holistic classroom to provide the missing guidance for our younger generation. The subject is timely and without question of paramount importance in today's health climate. Covering topics from nutrition and exercise to the psychology of self-image, LHT walks teens through their personal journey toward wholeness in a way that hasn't been seen in other programs.

Thank you Cynthia, for not only focusing on America's biggest health problem, youth obesity, but also for giving the problem an "Action Plan!"

Dr. Herb Akers DC CCN
Clinical Nutritionist

"Cynthia Besson has given a gift to the next generation with her LHT program, by putting the power in teen's hands to change their health drastically. There are very few dangers to health as pressing as obesity. We know that studies show that individuals who are obese as children are almost always obese as adults, so it's pivotal to intervene NOW. She is to be commended not only for her passion, but also because she has taken a dangerous health problem by the horns, addressed the cause of it, and helped to create a step by step plan for teens to make positive lifestyle changes and make them last."

Dr. Heather Wdowin, NMD

Teen Testimonials

Adrienne – 14 "I signed up for the program because I wanted to learn how to eat healthy and drop some weight so I could look like the rest of my friends. Over the course of 2.5 months, I lost 17lbs, became the fastest person on my soccer team and felt comfortable in my body for the first time in my life. It's been 4 years since LHT and I still incorporate what I learned into my daily lifestyle."

Kyrsta – 15 "I learned that I eat a lot of times when I'm not even hungry and the program taught me to be more aware of my feelings. I know I am addicted to sugar and carbohydrates and I learned that in class. I also learned to look at my body in a different, more positive way. I am more than just a number on the scale!"

Sierra – 19 "Because I had a brain tumor when I was young, I have always had a hard time paying attention in class, but not LHT. I was fully involved and loved each class. I also surprised myself and when we were given the pedometers, I started walking 10,000 steps a day."

Nick – 13 "I was drinking a six pack of soda a day when I started the program. Seeing how much sugar is in a soda was a total shocker to me! I cut back A LOT on my portions and started walking and even running. I really just didn't believe I could make some of the changes I did. It was really cool and I liked the fieldtrips with the group too. My mom and I BOTH lost weight on the program, so it's really helped my whole family."

Madison – 14 "I'm really an emotional eater (which I didn't know before LHT) and knew very little about what to eat. WOW, how I have changed. I loved the class, doing the vision boards and exercising with Kat. My Doctor flipped out, (in a good way) when I went for my check up and immediately asked for LHT's information!"

Parkyre – 13 "I realized that my portions were way off, so I cut back on those. I started drinking more water and working out more. Really enjoyed hanging out with the rest of the group during classes too. It was super fun! I've Lost 12 pounds so far and really learned a lot! (My parents own a great restaurant, so it's not easy!)"

"What would you attempt to do if you knew you would not fail?"

- Robert Schuller

Welcome to the Leaner Healthier Teen Revolution Program

We're honored you've chosen us to be a part of your life for the next six weeks. Our hope for you is that you achieve a healthy, happy, long, life.

As a formerly overweight teen myself I know the pain associated with being heavy. Like many of you, I struggled with diet after diet, only to gain the weight back. I studied healthcare and nursing, and quickly decided to go into the weight loss industry. I figured, if I learned all I could about weight loss, then maybe it would help me deal with my own weight challenges. Seven years later, I had learned a lot about diet and exercise and managed to lose a little weight myself, but still hadn't reached my goal.

It wasn't until years later - after having worked with almost all the giants in the weight loss industry and owning my own franchise weight loss and fitness center that I made the decision to take charge of my health and not just my *weight*, finally achieving my goal. I'm proud to say I lost forty pounds and have kept it off for over fifteen years! If there had been a program like LHT around when I was young, it wouldn't have taken me my entire career to get control of my weight. That is why I want this for you.

Background

In 2002, I was fortunate enough to meet Mr. World, Jimmy Badra. I was excited to learn that he and I shared similar values and beliefs about weight loss and fitness. Having both been overweight teens, we also knew of the pain and shame associated with being called fat. Committed to helping find a solution to the teen obesity epidemic plaguing our nation, we combined our backgrounds of more than forty years of health, fitness, and nutrition knowledge, to create the LHT (*Leaner Healthier Teen Revolution Program*).

The LHT program was co-created with the assistance of over forty teen volunteers, many of who participated in our focus groups and offered their support and advice. Numerous others went on to successfully lose weight, and of that we are truly proud!

We owe them a great deal of gratitude for hanging in there while LHT was taking shape. We are so proud of their accomplishments and willingness to share their personal challenges with us. It's because of their success that LHT is a reality.

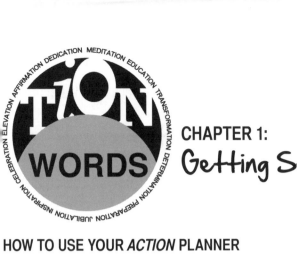

CHAPTER 1:
Getting Started

HOW TO USE YOUR *ACTION* PLANNER

Statistics show that people who keep a food diary are far more successful than those who don't. It's an absolute MUST for those who take fitness and weight loss seriously! That's why LHT created this unique **FOR TEENS ONLY** Action Planner!

It's important to record your eating and exercise habits as a way of keeping track of your progress. It's what we like to call a "reality check"! I mean let's be honest, how can you possibly remember what you ate last weekend?

Keeping a planner not only helps you see how much you REALLY ate, it also helps you identify what, when, where and why you ate!

Through the use of **action words** and phrases you'll learn many things about yourself and your weight which may surprise you!

As you work your way through your journal, be honest with yourself when going through the written exercises. Look at this journal as a success tool, not as homework. You've chosen LHT because you wanted to learn about losing weight, well here's your chance! If you are serious about learning, then you should take this journey seriously!

"LHTs live a leaner, longer life!"

"A journey of a thousand miles begins with a single step."
- Lao-tzu

LHT's SEVEN ACTIONS FOR SUCCESS

As you work through your **Action Plan**, you'll be mastering each section through the use of **ACTION WORDS**!

ACTION WORDS ARE WORDS THAT END IN T-I-O-N.

LHT believes **WORDS HAVE POWER** and so the **ACTION** words were born!

Action #1: MOTIVATION - You'll begin your LHT program by finding the motivation you need to get started!

Action #2: EDUCATION - Next, you'll be educated on the basics of nutrition!

Action #3: INSPIRATION - We all need a little Inspiration from time to time. We'll help you identify your support team and choose the right weight loss buddy.

Action #4: IMPLEMENTATION - Next, you'll be putting your plan into action by getting started on the LHT weight loss and fitness plan.

Action #5: AFFIRMATION - You'll learn how to visualize success by using affirmations to turn your dreams into reality.

Action #6: TEMPTATION - We'll teach you how to overcome temptations and deal with those emotional eating challenges we all face.

Action #7: CLARIFICATION - This final action will include reflection and clarification of what you've learned throughout your six week plan.

Have some fun while you're at it and see if you can find ALL **THE ACTION WORDS**. (There are about 300 of them!)

Follow these **SEVEN ACTIONS FOR SUCCESS** and you're certain to accomplish more than just your weight loss goals!

CHAPTER 2:

Understanding Your Weight

WHY AM I OVERWEIGHT IN THE FIRST PLACE?

An estimated sixty-five percent of adults (your parents) are overweight and if you're like millions of other teens who are reading this, then you probably weigh more than you should.

SO IT'S MY PARENTS FAULT THEN?

Some causes can be blamed on them. Things like genetics, passing on poor eating and fitness habits and allowing you to eat too much junk food. But you can't blame your parents altogether. Perhaps when you were younger you weren't able to choose what went in your mouth, but now as a teen you can!

There are several reasons for a weight challenge, but EATING TOO MUCH and NOT MOVING ENOUGH are TWO of the main reasons.

Our bodies weren't designed to eat high fat, processed, refined, and fried foods and then sit all day in school, in front of the TV or at a computer! Back in the cave-man days (before TV and computers) our bodies were designed to store fat so if we couldn't find food (while out hunting), we wouldn't starve! Our ancestors were constantly hunting and searching for food (exercise). Now we just stop by the store or go to a drive thru with little to no hunting involved!

Today our body weight is not only determined by our ancestors' genes, but by the lifestyle choices we make.

> *"All glory comes from daring to begin!"*
>
> - William Shakespeare

THE FIVE W'S OF EATING MAKE A GREAT IMPACT ON OUR HEALTH:

Who: Who we eat with can have a big impact on how much we eat.

What: The kind of food we eat is a huge factor in being overweight.

When: How often we eat and when we eat (frequently or not at all) affects our weight.

Where: Where we eat is also significant. If we're eating in front of the TV or computer all the time, or eating fast food on the run, this often leads to weight gain.

Why: If we're eating for emotional reasons and never learn why those emotions lead us to overeat, then we'll probably gain any lost weight back.

WHY DO I NEED TO LOSE WEIGHT ANYWAY?
Being overweight puts you at risk of developing diabetes, high blood pressure, high cholesterol, heart disease, stroke, gallbladder disease and certain types of cancer. And as you get older, you're potential of developing health problems as a result of being overweight increases substantially.

SO I CAN WORRY ABOUT THAT WHEN I GET OLDER?
Sadly, you can't! They're finding kids as young as nine with blocked arteries and high cholesterol! As many as one out of three new cases of diabetes are being diagnosed in children and adolescents. Recent statistics claim that one out of every three overweight teens will develop some form of diabetes in their lifetime. Seven percent of teens are pre-diabetic and more are headed in that direction. Obesity, if left untreated can take 10 to 20 years from your life.

SO WHAT DO I NEED TO DO TO LOSE WEIGHT?

It's like Dorothy in *The Wizard of Oz*, you've had the power right in front of you the whole time - you just didn't know how to use it!

So close your eyes and like Dorothy did, click your heals together three times, make a wish, and turn your dream into a reality by mastering LHT's Seven Actions for Success.

Sign the **declaration** on the next page and put it up somewhere you can read it everyday!

MY LEANER HEALTHIER TEEN REVOLUTION DECLARATION

I_____ , on this _____ day of _____ in
the year_____ am committed to following the six-week LHT action plan.

I promise I will learn the **Seven Actions for Success** and will practice them daily. I believe I can lose weight the healthy way and keep it off for life by learning to lead a healthier lifestyle.

I realize this is an action plan I can use in all areas of my life and will do my best to put the things I've learned on this program into action!

I agree that only I and I alone can choose to lose weight. I am choosing to do this program because I am committed to my health. I understand that losing weight is a byproduct of getting healthy and that if I make health my number one focus, I will lose the weight!

I know that learning to take charge of my emotions is an important part of taking control of my weight. I promise I will learn new ways to move my body, educate my mind, and heal my emotions.

I believe that **WORDS HAVE POWER** and agree to use only positive words and affirmations and be kind to myself throughout my LHT journey. I will examine my feelings about myself and my weight honestly and am willing to change those beliefs that don't serve me in a healthy manner.

I agree that I deserve to be at a healthy weight for life. I am totally capable of achieving any goal I set my mind to, including this one. I am totally worth it. I am one of a kind. I am worthy of success. I congratulate myself in advance for creating a new healthier lifestyle. I say, "thank you," to myself for loving me enough to change.

Date:_____

Signed:_____

"With love and patience, nothing is impossible."
- Daisaku Ikeda

5

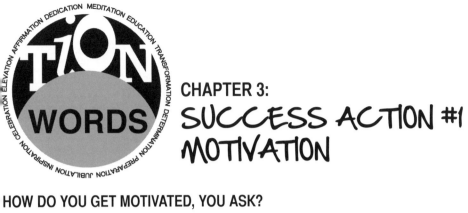

CHAPTER 3

SUCCESS ACTION #1 MOTIVATION

HOW DO YOU GET MOTIVATED, YOU ASK?

Well you've already taken the first step by signing your Leaner Healthier Teen Revolution Declaration. Making the decision to lose weight is usually the hardest step. Now that you've made that commitment, we'll help you do the rest.

We've created some great goal-setting and visualization exercises to help you strengthen your motivation and reach your goals!

COMPLETING SUCCESS ACTION #1 WILL HELP YOU:
- Find your personal motivation for losing weight.
- Set your action goals for the next six weeks.
- Learn about your self-perception versus body-perception.
- Master the technique of visualizing success.

Now it's your turn to be an LHT success story!

Motivation is one of those unique things that can only come from inside you. True, others can motivate you, (like your LHT Coach,) but the truth is that when you desire something from the bottom of your heart, and do the work it takes, the entire universe will help you achieve that goal! The more you **BELIEVE** in the process, the more you will attract it towards you. (You've attracted this program to you, so your headed in the right direction!)

ACTION GOALS

Before you start, please read and commit to the following action goals:

I **commit** to recording in my **LHT action** planner daily.

I **commit** to doing **3 Physical Actions** from the **PA** list daily, (sweaty stuff) and **3 Extra Physical Actions** weekly, (easy stuff) from the **EPA** list.

I **commit** to saying my positive **affirmations** out loud, 10 times every morning.

I **commit** to educating myself about my body's **nutritional** needs and my hearts **emotional** needs.

I **commit** to looking at this program as part of a journey and not a **destination** (because eating healthy takes more than just six weeks).

I **commit** to choose and allow my **Support Team** to help me through my six week action plan.

I **commit** to telling my support team (friends and family), what I need from them to be **successful**.

I **commit** to **trying** new foods and new activities which I may not have tried before.

I **commit** to stopping the program and telling someone, if at any time I am not eating in a **healthy way**.

Date:_____

Signed: _____

"If you don't know where you're going,
any road will take you there."

- Doug Horton

CHAPTER 4:

SELF-PERCEPTION vs. BODY-PERCEPTION

Before you choose your goal weight, it's important you know the difference between self-perception and body-perception.

Self-Perception has to do with how you see yourself on the **INSIDE** - the parts of you that make up your mind and spirit. You know - the part that is uniquely you!

Body-perception is strictly how you see your body on the **OUTSIDE** (the way you see it in your head)! The person you see when you look into the mirror.

LET'S CLEARLY DEFINE THE TWO!

You are NOT what you weigh. Weight is clearly and simply a number on a scale. It does not, nor will it ever, define **WHO you are on the *inside*.** Only **you** can define that! The way you see BOTH your self-perception and your body-perception will make a dramatic difference in your success, both now and for the rest of your life. We think that's pretty important!

Many weight loss programs work only on body-perception, but LHT knows that true lasting success must include both!

WHAT ARE YOUR CURRENT BODY-PERCEPTIONS?

Did you know that fifty percent of teenagers are dissatisfied with their body image? If you're reading this book, you're probably one of them. Unfortunately, you are growing up in a world increasingly focused on the importance of appearance. That leads to unnecessary pressure to be thin! This pressure can come from many sources:

Parents:
We all learn certain elements of body-perception from our parents. If your parents make a negative comment about your weight, it effects how you see yourself. These

9

comments can be internalized and confused with your self-perception. So you may equate a statement like, "You need to lose some weight," to mean, "I'm fat and worthless." This is simply not true! You may be overweight on the outside, but that has nothing to do with your inside!

"Anything you can conceive and believe, you can achieve!"
- Napoleon Hill

Peers:
Studies show that social comparison begins in kids as early as elementary school. Peers can be really hard on kids they think are overweight. Teasing can have long-term effects on our self-perception (internal) which can lead to a destruction of our body-perception (external). Teasing can also lead to depression and eating disorders (more on that later).

Media:
No influence here right? NOT! The influence of media on our body-perception is powerful. Just look at Lady Gaga or any music video and you'll see what I mean. We see skewed images on T.V and in magazines all the time. When you compare yourself to Victoria Secret models and celebrities, no wonder you feel dissatisfied! Those images are not real! They're airbrushed, cropped and digitized! It's not reality, it's perception! Just like you may perceive your own body incorrectly, isn't it possible you are seeing the media images through rose colored glasses? Take your glasses off and look at them getting out of bed at 6:30 in the morning. I promise you they don't look that way!

Sadly, all of these influences affect how we see ourselves. Each has its own perceived reality, but it's important to distinguish **true reality from perceived reality**.

Parents:
Your Perceived Reality: "They think I'm fat, so they must think I'm worthless too."
Their TRUE Reality: "I'm scared you're carrying too much weight and it's affecting your health. I don't want you to get diabetes. I love you and I can tell you're unhappy. It hurts me to see you hurting. I've suffered from being overweight and I don't want that for you. As your parent, I feel responsible and I don't know how to help you.

Peers:
Your Perceived Reality: "They don't like me because I'm fat."
Their TRUE Reality: They are not intelligent enough to say anything else. They don't care about others' feelings because they're selfish. The only way they get

attention is to make fun of others. They have a strong need to be in control. They're afraid of what others will think of them.

Media:
Your Perceived Reality: "Thin is in." "Appearances are everything."
TRUE Reality: The average woman in America is a size 14! We keep growing. Appearances are fleeting, we all grow old. It's through the eyes we see one's soul, and through one's **words and actions**, we learn their true character.

VISUALIZATION CAN HELP CHANGE PERCEPTION
One of the things I attribute my weight loss success to is visualization. All of us visualize, all the time, about everything. From small things like what you're going to eat for lunch to big things like the reaction your best friend would have if you told them you saw their girl/boyfriend kissing someone else (*SEE your doing it right now*)!

Successful people imagine and visualize constantly! Walt Disney and Steve Jobs are great examples of people who used their imaginations. Don't you think Walt visualized and imagined Disneyland before it was built? Steve Jobs imagined everyone using a computer some day. Everything we do starts with a thought. We are the only ones responsible for our thoughts. No one can control our minds.

Have you ever visualized or imagined something and *then it happened*?

HOW CAN I USE VISUALIZATION TO HELP ME LOSE WEIGHT?
Simple! Start by imagining yourself at your goal weight feeling proud, strong and unstoppable!

The key to successful visualization is to **think, speak, and act** as if it has already happened. Did you know the mind cannot tell the difference from what is vividly imagined and what is real? If you've ever had a bad dream or pictured a horrible situation, than you know what I mean!

Start by closing your eyes and making your own movie! Ask yourself: What are you doing? Who are you with? What are you wearing? How do you feel?

"It's kinda fun to do the impossible."

- Walt Disney

Use this visualization script to get you started:

Visualizing Myself at Goal! *(Fill in the blanks)*

I'm at my goal weight of _____pounds.

I'm wearing a size_____and feeling_____.

I finally fit into my_____and I look_____.

I walk into school at size _____, wearing my_____and

feel _____. My Friends all notice how

_____I look and tell me _____. That

makes me feel_____.

My family is so_____of me. My_____

hugs me and gives me a_____.

I can't wait for_____.

Make up your own movie and watch it every night before you go to sleep. Remember, the mind can't tell the difference from what is vividly imagined and what is real!

My Before and After Pictures

BEFORE	AFTER

(Paste your before and after pictures in the boxes above.)

"Courage is the capacity to confront what can be imagined."

- Leo Rosten

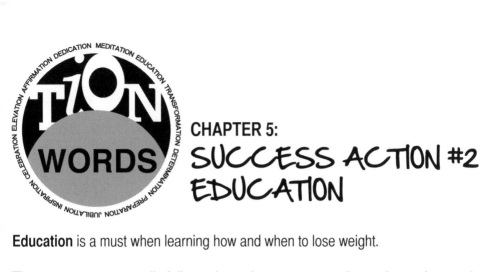

CHAPTER 5:

SUCCESS ACTION #2 EDUCATION

Education is a must when learning how and when to lose weight.

There are so many so-called diet and exercise programs on the market and so much **information**; it can be overwhelming (and dangerous).

No wonder we're all confused. Have you ever heard the saying, "knowledge is power"? Well, if you are going to conquer anything in life you must first LEARN as much as you can about the subject! Knowledge in many ways allows you to take control of the situation. So let's start by educating ourselves on the basics of **nutrition**.

> **COMPLETING SUCCESS ACTION #2 WILL HELP YOU:**
> • **Understand Basic Nutrition.**
> • **The difference between Simple Carbs and Complex Carbs.**
> • **About Insulin and Diabetes.**

NUTRITION IS LIKE A CAR

What kind of car do you see yourself as? A Mercedes, a Jaguar, or are you more like a burned out van?

I often refer to our bodies being like a car. When you think about it, they really are our only form of transportation! You wouldn't put low octane gas in a sports car and expect it to run well because the fuel itself can't power a high-performance engine. Yet, we put low quality food in our bodies all the time and wonder why they're breaking down. Putting cheap gasoline in a car will make it perform badly. Putting bad food in our bodies in the form of sugar, white flour, grease, chips, soda and candy will make our bodies perform badly. In addition, if we put in premium healthy foods into our bodies, they will perform at peak performance, just like our cars!

So, if our bodies are like cars, and food is our gasoline, than insulin would be the oil.

Too much or too little oil and the car won't run the way it's supposed to! Too much or too little insulin can have the same effect on your body and can become a serious problem that can lead to diabetes. If you go too long with bad oil, eventually you'll have to replace the engine, right?

Some foods digest quicker than others into our bloodstream, causing our body's insulin levels to rise too quickly. This can cause mood swings, hunger, fatigue, and weight gain. These "quick digesting" carbohydrates are known as SIMPLE carbs and those that digest more slowly (like apples and whole wheat) are known as COMPLEX carbs.

The LHT plan is based on a healthy diet designed specifically with your car's oil pump, (the body's insulin) in mind.

Managing these SIMPLE carbs and getting in more COMPLEX carbs will help you cut cravings, minimize hunger and help you lose weight. Insulin controls the storage of fat and is involved in releasing energy, and controlling our appetite. **Insulin affects each and every cell in your body**. We all need insulin to live, but **too much insulin can have negative consequences, including diabetes, high blood pressure, obesity and heart disease**.

Protein has minimal impact on insulin and fat has no effect. Therefore, lower levels of carbohydrate intake, combined with adequate protein intake, help control weight by reducing excess insulin. When you control your carb intake, your body begins to use its stored fat for fuel.

LHT knows that as teens you have unique nutritional needs, so we designed the plan with many of the following essential needs in mind:

- You're still growing, so you need a certain amount of calories and nutrients per day to be healthy.
- Most experts believe a teen should not diet because they will feel deprived and just gain more weight.

Don't worry; we have given you lots of the foods you requested, so you won't feel deprived!

- Most of our teens did better with a more controlled carbohydrate diet. We are not against carbs (in fact you'll see many on the plan), we just know that certain carbs can actually make you hungrier and more crabby, and can wreak havoc on your car's oil system.

CHAPTER 6:

SUCCESS ACTION #3 IMPLEMENTATION

Implementation means it's time to put what you've learned into ACTION!

COMPLETING SUCCESS ACTION #3 WILL HELP YOU:

- Determine your BMI (Body Mass Index).
- START LOSING WEIGHT.
- Learn how to keep track of what you eat.
- Learn how to get physical (PA's & EPA's).

These meal plans are estimates "ONLY" of what a daily menu could look like. As you know from class, we don't really want you to count calories, but we do want you to learn what a menu and serving size looks like!

The LHT Revolution Weight Loss Plan FOOD EXCHANGE LIST

Categories: Veggies • Dairy • Fruits • Protein • Starches • Fats

All the foods within each category can be exchanged for one another, within the same category. Use these lists to pick something you like for your menu. For example, if you don't want to eat broccoli then pick something else from your veggie list.

Veggies: Most vegetables have about 25 calories and 15 grams of carbohydrates per serving. A veggie serving size is measured as follows:

1/2 cup	Any cooked vegetables (carrots, broccoli, zucchini, cabbage, etc...)
1 cup	Any raw vegetables or salad greens
1/2 cup	Vegetable juice

LHT believes you can never have too many veggies so if you're hungry eat away!

15

Dairy: Most dairy has about 90 calories per serving. A dairy serving size is measured as follows:

1 cup	Milk, fat-free or 1% fat
3/4 cup	Yogurt, plain non fat or low fat (Check the sugar!) 10 to 15 grams please
1/2 cup	Low fat ice cream or frozen yogurt
1TBSP	Cream

Protein: Most lean (lean = lower in fat) protein has approximately 100 calories and approx 3-5 grams of fat per serving. A protein serving size is measured as follows:

3 ounces	Turkey or chicken breast, white meat is better, no skin
3 ounces	Fish (halibut, cod, sole, flounder)
3 ounces	Whole egg
3 ounces	Canned tuna in water, no oil please
3 ounces	Shellfish (clams, lobster, scallop, shrimp)
3/4 cup	Cottage cheese, non fat or low fat
2 each	Egg whites
1/4 cup	Egg substitute
1 ounce	Fat-free or low fat cheese, mozzarella, ricotta, feta
4 ounces	Tofu
3 ounces	Lean ground beef
1 piece	Low fat bacon or sausage (also a fat!)
1 each	Hot dog or turkey dog

Fruit: Most fruits have about 60-70 calories and 5 grams of carbohydrates. A fruit serving is measured as follows:

1 sm/med	Apples, banana, orange, nectarine, pear, peach, kiwi, plums, pineapple, mangoes, papaya
1 small box	Raisins
15	Cherries
1/2	Grapefruit
1/2	Mango
1 cup	Fresh berries (strawberries, raspberries or blueberries)

16

1 cup	Fresh melon (cut in cubes)
1/8 th	Cantaloupe or Honeydew melon
4 ounces	Unsweetened Juice
4 tsp	Jelly or Jam

Starches: Most starches have about 80-100 calories and approximately 15-20 grams of carbohydrates. A starch serving is measured as follows:

1 slice	Bread (white, pumpernickel, whole wheat, rye, spelt)
2 slices	Reduced calorie or "light" bread
1/2	Bagels (SMALL) - get the minis!
1 small	Whole wheat tortilla (not the gigantic ones)
1/2 small	Hamburger bun
3/4 cup	Most cold cereals (watch the sugar 10-15 grams only)
1/3 cup	Rice, brown or white, Barley or couscous or Bulgar (cooked)
1/2 cup	Corn, sweet potato, or green peas
1/2 small	Baked sweet or white potato
15 small	Pretzels
3 cups	Popcorn, microwave (no butter, light only)

These examples below are based on three different types of food cravings: salt, sugar and fat. If you are someone who craves sugar for instance, it would help you feel more satisfied and not deprived by having a few sweet things throughout the day on your plan.

1600-1700 Calorie Fat Craver Plan	Calories	Eat this item or choose an item from your exchange list
BREAKFAST: Whole wheat toast, 1 slice	75	(1 Starch)
I Can't Believe It's Not Butter spray	40	(1 Fat)
Fried Egg (any style)	95	(1 Protein)
Milk, skim or soy 1 cup	100	(1 Dairy)
Orange	80	(1 Fruit)
LUNCH BREAK SNACK: 4 oz low fat string Cheese	150	(1 Dairy, 1 Protein)
TOTAL CALORIES	**540**	

LUNCH: Subway TM Club Salad	150	(2 Protein, 2 Veggies)
Subway fat free salad dressing	70	(1 Starch)
Subway soup (Clam Chowder or broccoli & cheese)	170	(1 Starch, 1 1/2 Fat)
Ice tea or diet soda	0	(Free)
TOTAL CALORIES	**390**	

DINNER: Skillet Meals (Pesto Chicken Primavera)	230	(2 Starch, 1 Protein)
Broccoli 1 cup cooked	60	(1 Veggie)
Salad with everything	100	(1 Veggie)
Non-fat salad dressing	30	(Free)
Water or diet soda	0	(Free)
TOTAL CALORIES	**420**	

Daily Snacks: LHT snack bar or shake, low fat string cheese, low fat yogurt, 2 tbsp walnuts, 1/4 avocado, fruit.	210	You can have 2 servings "any time" per day
TOTAL CALORIES	**715**	

DESSERT: Frozen fruit bar with cream	85	(1 Fruit, 1 Fat)

TOTAL CALORIES DAY   **1645**

FAT CRAVER EXCHANGE LIST:

Here are some exchange suggestions you can use if you are someone who craves fatty foods.

McDonald's Egg McMuffin (Eat only 1/2 the bread part =1 starch 1 protein 1 fat)
Low fat sour cream (1 TBSP= 1 Fat)
Cream cheese (1 TBSP = 1 Fat)
Avocado (1/4 = 1 Fat)
Sugar free ice cream (1/2 Cup = 1 Dairy 1 Fat)
Any low fat cheese (pair of dice size = 1 Protein 1 Fat)
Cool Whip (2 TBSP = 1 Fat)
Sugar free pudding cup (2 Fat)

Eat this item or an item from 1600-1700 Calorie Sugar Craver Plan	Calories	choose your exchange list
BREAKFAST: Whole wheat toast, 1 slice	75	(1 Starch)
Jelly, low sugar or sugar free 2 tsp.	20	(1/2 Fruit)
Apple Jacks cereal , 1/2 cup	65	(1 Starch)
Milk, skim or soy 1 cup	100	(1 Dairy)
Orange Juice , 3/4 cup	80	(1 1/2 Fruit)
LUNCH BREAK SNACK: Starbucks Soy Cappuccino (Small) YUMMY!	80	(1 Dairy)
TOTAL CALORIES	**420**	

LUNCH: Subway Club Salad	150	(2 Protein, 2 Veggies)
Subway fat free salad dressing	70	(1 Starch)
Subway Fruizle (Sunrise Refresher)	120	(1 Starch, 1 Fruit)
Ice tea or diet soda	0	(Free)
TOTAL CALORIES	**340**	

DINNER: Baked chicken, 6 oz	200	(2 Protein)
Vegetable oil, 1 tsp	60	(1 1/2 Fat)
I Can't Believe It's Not Butter spray	20	(1 Fat)
Broccoli or other veggie 1/2 cup	60	(1 Veggie)
Salad with everything	100	(1 Veggie)
Non-fat salad dressing	30	(Free)
Water or diet soda	0	(Free)
Daily Snacks: LTG snack bar or shake, low fat yogurt, Quaker chocolate rice cakes, fruit.	350	You can have 2 servings "any time" per day
TOTAL CALORIES	**820**	

DESSERT: Healthy Choice Fudge bar	80	(1 Starch)

TOTAL CALORIES DAY   **1695**

19

SUGAR CRAVER EXCHANGE LIST:

Here are some exchange suggestions you can use if you are someone (like me) who craves sweet sugary things!

Healthy Choice Sugar free Ice cream (1/2 cup = 1 Dairy 1 Fat)
West Soy, Chocolate milk (1/2 cup = 1 Protein 1 Dairy)
Cinnamon toast (Splenda and cinnamon) (1 slice = 1 Starch)
LHT Bar™ or shake (1 = 1 Protein 1 Starch)
Low fat Ice cream (1/2 cup = 1 Fat)
Chocolate rice cakes with low fat peanut butter (7 small cakes = 1 Starch 1 TBSP PB = 1 Protein 1 Fat)

1600-1700 Calorie Salt Craver Plan	Calories	Eat this item or choose an item from your exchange list
BREAKFAST: Whole wheat toast, 1 slice	75	(1 Starch)
I Can't Believe It's Not Butter spray	40	(1 Fat)
Egg (any style)	95	(1 Protein)
Milk, skim or soy 1 cup	100	(1 Dairy)
Orange	80	(1 Fruit)
LUNCH BREAK SNACK: 7 Quaker Sour Cream and Onion rice cakes & 4 oz low fat cheese	150	(1 Starch, 1 Dairy)
TOTAL CALORIES	**540**	

LUNCH: Subway Club Salad	150	(2 Protein, 2 Veggies)
Subway fat free salad dressing	70	(1 Starch)
Subway Fritos original chips (small bag)	100	(1 Starch, 1 Fat)
Iced tea or diet soda	0	(Free)
TOTAL CALORIES	**340**	

DINNER: Baked chicken, 3 oz	155	(1 Protein)
Vegetable oil, 1 tsp	60	(1 Fat)
I Can't Believe It's Not Butter spray	40	(1 Fat)
Broccoli or other veggie 1/2 cup cooked	60	(1 Veggie)
Salad with everything	100	(1 Veggie)
Non-fat salad dressing	30	(Free)
Water or diet soda	0	(Free)

Daily Snacks: LTG snack bar or shake, low fat cheese, popcorn, pumpkin seeds, fruit.	210	You can have 2 servings any time each day
TOTAL CALORIES	**650**	

DESSERT: Sugar free Oatmeal cookies 2	120	(1 Starch, 1 Fat)

TOTAL CALORIES DAY   1655

SALT CRAVER EXCHANGE LIST:
Here are some additional SALTY suggestions you can use if you are a salt craver!

Quaker Sour Cream and Onion rice cakes (7 = 1 Starch)
Low fat cheese (size of pair of dice= 1 Dairy)
Healthy Choice Sugar free oatmeal cookie (1 = 1 Starch)
Taco Bell Chicken Gordita Supreme (1 Starch, 1 Fat, 1 Protein)
Popcorn (1 cup = 1 Starch)
Pumpkin seeds (small bag = 1 Protein)
Sugar-free sour candy (Small bag= 1 Starch)
Beef jerky (Small bag = 1 Protein)

READING FOOD LABELS
On the back of most foods you'll find a nutrition label. Below we've explained what each of those items mean. We recommend you look at several things when reading a label.

1.) Calories
2.) Total Carbohydrates
3.) Sugar
4.) Sodium
5.) Fat

Nutrition Facts

Serving Size 1 cup (228 g)		
Servings per Container 2		Start here
Amount per serving		
Calories 250	Calories from Fat 110	Check calories
	% Daily Value	
Total Fat 12 g	18%	
Saturated Fat 3 g	15%	
Trans Fat 3 g		
Cholesterol 30 mg	10%	
Sodium 470 mg	20%	Limit these
Total Carbohydrate 31 g	20%	
		Get enough of these
Dietary Fiber 0 g		
Sugars 5 g		
Protein 5 g		
Vitamin A 4%	Vitamin C 2%	
Calcium 20%	Iron 4%	

* Percent Daily Values are based on a 2,000 calorie diet. You Daily Values may be higher or lower depending on your calorie needs

Using a Label to Make Other Healthful Food Choices

• Choose foods containing the most FIBER.
• Keep SATURATED FAT as low as you can.
• Avoid TRANS FAT.
• Look for the lowest amount of SODIUM.
• Read the INGREDIENTS to help choose healthy foods.

Reading a Food Label

• Start with the **SERVING SIZE.** All the listed nutrients are based on this serving size.
• Note that **SERVINGS PER CONTAINER** equals the number of servings contained in the package.

Using a Label to Count Carbohydrates
• Look at **TOTAL CARBOHYDRATE** per serving
• 1 Carbohydrate Choice = 15 grams of carbohydrate

Range of Total Carbohydrate grams per Carbohydrate (CHO) Choice
11-20 gms = 1 CHO choice
21-25 gms = 1 ½ CHO choice
26-35 gms = 2 CHO choice
36-40 gms = 2 ½ CHO choice
41-50 gms = 3 CHO choice
51-55 gms = 3½ CHO choice
56-65 gms = 4 CHO choice
66-70 gms = 4 ½ CHO choice
71-80 gms = 5 CHO choice

• SUGARS are included in the total grams of carbohydrate.
• If FIBER is 5 grams or more, you may subtract half the total grams of fiber from the total grams of carbohydrate before using the table above.

BASIC TERMS:

Serving Size: The "serving size" on a food label defines the amount of food you should eat in one sitting. For example, if you are eating cereal and it's says 1/2 cup, that's the suggested serving size. If you eat a CUP of cereal (which most of us often do, then you are actually eating TWO servings (which means double the calories - Sneaky!)

Calories: The number of calories refers to the amount of calories contained in a single serving. This can be tricky when you get a super size bag of cookies or chips, so look closely. The calories may say 120 per serving, but the servings per container is THREE! So it's not just 120 calories, its 120 x 3 servings = 360 calories! (Yikes!)

Total Fat: This refers to the total number of fat grams including: saturated, monounsaturated and polyunsaturated. The total calories from fat are determined by multiplying the number of fat grams by nine (a gram of fat contains nine calories per serving). So, multiply the numbers of fat grams by nine then compare that number with the total calories on the label. This tells you how much of the food your eating is fat.

Saturated Fat: This is the fat that clogs your arteries and increases your risk for heart disease and other major illnesses. Saturated fat is part of the total fat in food, but it gets listed separately because it's so bad for you. We should all avoid foods that are high in saturated fat. Hamburgers, for instance, have a lot of what we call saturated or bad fat, whereas chicken is leaner and doesn't have as much saturated fat, especially if it's the light colored meat, like chicken breasts.

Sodium: Salt is labeled as sodium. It is recommended our daily intake be at about 2,400 milligrams or less. Teens should average 2,200 to 2,400. Most teens are getting in twice that much in their daily intake which contributes to young people having high blood pressure.

Total Carbohydrate: The total carb line shows the amount of carbs in a single serving. This includes both simple carbs (fast acting sugars) and complex carbs (slow acting sugars). Listed underneath total carbohydrate are sugars. This tells you how much sugar is in a serving of that particular food. You can figure out how much complex carbohydrates are in the food by subtracting the difference between the two: total carbohydrate - sugars = complex carbohydrates. A gram of carbohydrates has 4 calories per serving. COMPLEX IS BEST, so you want that number to be higher than the sugars!

Sugar: The amount of sugar that is in a serving.
Protein: This tells you how many grams of protein per single serving. A serving of protein has 4 calories.

Dietary Fiber: Just underneath total carbohydrate is dietary fiber. It's recommended that we eat foods with at least 3 grams of fiber per serving. This is helpful when trying to lose weight because fiber fills us up, helps control blood sugar, and helps keep your body's waste management system running smoothly (slightly important thing). It's also known to reduce the risk of heart disease, bowel disease, and certain cancers. You should try to get at least 25 to 35 grams in per day.

Percent Daily Values: Percent Daily Values is based on a 2,000-calorie diet. These percentages tell you how much of the RDA (recommended daily allowance) for each nutrient is present in a single serving.

WHAT DOES A SERVING SIZE LOOK LIKE?

Starch/Carbs
A slice of bread is about the size of a cassette tape
Small bagel is about the size of the top of a peanut butter jar
1/2 cup rice or pasta fits into a large cupcake wrapper
1 cup is about the size of a baseball
Fruit
1 medium is about the size of a tennis ball
Vegetables
1 cup cooked is about the size of a baseball
Protein
1 oz. cheese is equal to a pair of dice
Serving of meat / protein is the size of a computer mouse
1 oz. of any nuts is the size of a golf ball

"An error is not a mistake until you refuse to correct it."
- Unknown

PORTION TRICKS
Say you're at a friend's party or better yet, you're out at a nice restaurant, how do you measure your food?
"Oh excuse me waiter, do you have a scale?"
I don't think so. Here are some of LHT's favorite portion tricks!

Trick #1: Be a **SMART SECTIONer!**
Divide your plate into four even **sections**, kind of like a clock.
Section one should include a serving of protein,
Section two, a serving of carbs,
Section three, veggies,
Section four, a fruit.
Now doesn't that seem a lot easier to remember and a lot less embarrassing?

Trick #2: **ALWAYS** order your salad dressing on the side! This way you can control how much goes on. You can also do this for things like cheese in your omelet, sour cream, mayonnaise and anything else that might have a high fat content you can control.

Trick #3: **ASK** and you shall receive! If you want a two egg omelet, ASK! If you want a tuna (turkey) sandwich with no mayo, ASK! If you want a Cobb salad with no blue cheese, ASK! Most restaurants are happy to please!

Trick #4: **DOGGIE BAG** it and stop when you're full or if your portion size is too big. Why not take some home for your pet (only if it's healthy for them, of course) or have it for lunch the next day.

Trick #5: **SHARE IT** with a friend. I like to do this with desert. Besides it's fun to share and afterwards you'll be happy you did!

An easy way to remember the tricks?
SMART SECTIONERS *ALWAYS - ASK – your DOGGIE - to SHARE it.*

FYI: If your dinner plate and your cereal bowl are extra-large, than you will tend to want to fill them up. A really great **EASY** trick is to use a smaller bowl and plate. It really is a mind- game sometimes, and as far as finishing everything on your plate well...you really should only eat until you are full! I use a coffee mug to put my ice cream in, instead of a bowl. This works really well for both your mind and your body!

Did you know ... it takes **20 minutes** for the brain to tell the stomach it's full? That's why at Thanksgiving by the time the actual turkey comes out, we are full, right!?! So when you're eating, make sure to **SLOW DOWN** and chew your food. I promise you, you will get fuller faster. Another trick is to put your fork down after every bite. It takes a LONG time to eat the meal. Your friends and family might be irritated, but it works!!!

CHAPTER 7:
EXERCISE, WHO ME?

Exercise is an important part of any weight loss and maintenance program. Being fit is one of the most important keys to being healthy!

LHT thinks the word exercise has been given a bad rap, so we're changing it (because WORDS HAVE POWER) to **Physical Actions, (PA's)** and **Extra Physical Actions (EPA's).**

- **PA's** are activities you do **three times a week** or more for at least 20 minutes – things like aerobics, treadmill, weights, step, jogging etc...

- **EPA's** are things you do **daily** to burn calories, like walking up the stairs or cleaning your room, raking your yard, or washing the car (Yes, that's exercise!).

DO I HAVE TO BE PHYSICALLY ACTIVE?
Only if you want to keep losing weight and keep it off for life.

- People who exercise regularly lose more weight and keep it off longer than people who don't.

- Fitness improves your confidence and self esteem.

- Dieting without exercise can result in a loss of both fatty tissue and muscle, whereas exercise and strength training result in fat loss and rarely lean muscle loss. Let me put it this way, do you want to be thin and flabby, or fit and fabulous?

- Building and maintaining muscles helps to re-shape and re-sculpt your body. It also increases your body's metabolic rate (which means you're burning more calories, so you can eat more).

WHAT'S THE SECRET TO LIKING EXERCISE?

Secret #1: Internal (not external) **Motivation** is one of my secrets to long term fitness! Each of us has a force within us that motivates us to succeed. It's just a matter of finding a good enough reason to succeed. If your reasons for fitness are strong enough, then anything is possible! Let me give you an example: **If I told you I would give you a million dollars if you worked out every day for a month, what would you say?**

See what I mean? You just need a strong enough reason!

What's your number one reason to put fitness first in your life?

_____

Secret #2: Did you know that **LOVE is a verb?** That means that LOVE is an **action word!** But, do we always feel like doing something loving like cleaning the house or saying I love you? No, but sometimes when you just GO AHEAD and DO something loving, that feeling of love often comes after, right!?!

Exercise is the same way. It's a verb. You don't always feel like doing it, but sometimes you just need to GO AHEAD and DO it and the feeling will come after! **DON'T THINK ABOUT IT - JUST DO THE ACTION AND THE FEELING WILL FOLLOW!**

Secret #3: Find reasons *other than weight loss,* to exercise! Yes, I mean other than burning calories for the sake of burning calories. Don't get me wrong, you want to burn those calories, but if you exercise for two hours and only burn 300 calories you may give up. If you're exercising for other reasons like: it will help you live longer, or the fact that it helps condition your heart and lungs you may keep going. It sure helps me when I don't feel like it!

Also, it improves your circulation and blood glucose levels and makes you feel good because it increases your level of serotonin (a neurotransmitter which makes you calmer and happier).

Write down what your other reasons are for getting into shape. Are they powerful enough to get you to follow through, or are they weak?

_____

Hope you've got some good reasons because it's time to take **ACTION!**

Organization:
Making a plan for fitness is pivotal to success. One of my favorite sayings is, **"Failing to plan is planning to fail."** People who have a commitment to fitness plan it into their daily schedules. It's not a coincidence that they bring their lunch to school or go to the gym every day, it's planned! It takes twenty-eight days to create a habit. Why not make a twenty-eight day fitness commitment and see how you change?

Inspiration:
We all know that working out with a group or buddy increases your likelihood of success, that's one of the reasons we created the LHT buddy plan. So find someone who'll work out with you! Hey it doesn't even have to be a person, it can be your pet! My dog Parker loves to go walking (it's actually more like him pulling me) with me.

Visualization:
Imagination is a powerful motivator! The "movie in my mind" game has helped many an athlete and superstar achieve peak performance. Imagine you are Sylvester Stallone in Rocky. Imagine you are trying out for the Dallas Cowboy Cheerleaders or a Broadway play. Imagine you're skating at the Olympics or dancing in a music video. What ever it is that will motivate your mind to stimulate your body is a win!

Recreation:
How about doing something fun like biking, dancing, hiking or skating? Try listening to your favorite music while you're working out. Try skipping or jumping on a trampoline; it's hard to frown when you're jumping up and down! Fitness is forever, so we might as well do something we enjoy!

Excuse Elimination:
We have great excuses why we CAN'T exercise. How about, "I don't have the time to," "I don't have the energy," "I don't care, bad weather, bad hair day, (I use that one), I don't feel good or, I already worked out at school (sound familiar? I have more...). Don't be a DRAMA QUEEN! Be accountable for the goals you set for yourself. People that succeed don't except excuses from themselves. They make a decision and then take **ACTION!**

WHAT DOES FITNESS DO FOR ME ANYWAY?
Being Physical Burns Calories: Physical actions use up excess calories that would otherwise be stored as fat.

Being Physical Helps Raise Your Metabolism: The higher your metabolic rate, the more calories you burn, the easier it will be to lose weight.

Being Physical Reduces Fat and Increases Muscle: A pound of muscle burns 45 calories, a pound of fat burns 4! (Now that's a good reason to have more muscle!) Muscle cells are eight times more metabolically active than fat cells.

Being Physical Makes Losing Weight Easier: When you've just run a mile, you're less likely to cheat on something unhealthy. Working out also helps mentally because it releases endorphins in the brain that make us feel happy and content. When your emotions are in check, it makes it easier to stick to the plan!

Being Physical Makes You Stronger: Fitness gives you more confidence and greater stamina. It's exciting to see your body reshape itself due to working out. Looking at your body changing is a much better way to measure your progress than just the scale! Getting active increases your self-perception and makes you feel like you can do anything!

Regular Physical Action is important in losing weight and keeping it off! It helps prevent disease and improves your overall health. It helps your mind function better and your heart beat stronger! It doesn't matter what types of *physical actions* you perform – whether it be sports, yoga, walking, yard work, or rollerblading, even walking up the stairs is beneficial. Studies show that even as little as thirty minutes or more of physical activity per day can assist you in losing weight.

Don't forget to set **realistic goals** when you are starting a workout. Don't try to conquer the world and go out on a 20 mile run your first week. You can start by putting on your pedometer and walking some extra steps each day. What about trying a yoga or dance class? How about karate or swimming lessons?

"We can do anything we want to if we stick to it long enough"

\- Helen Keller

Do what you love and do it often. If you don't like something, remember, it takes 21 to 28 days to create a habit, so hang in there. I promise you if you become **physically active** for three weeks, you **WILL** start to enjoy it and absolutely notice a change! If you think you don't have enough time, notice how much time you are spending watching T.V., talking, texting or emailing! Put on your exercise clothes and tennis shoes as soon as you get home from school. Eat your snack, because I know you are probably starving and immediately go work out. Open your **mind, arms and heart** to new things and new people.

EXCUSE ELIMINATION

1. Write down all of the excuses you give yourself for **NOT working out**. Remember to include your emotional excuses as well, like fear, lack of motivation, and any insecurity about exercise you may have.

_____

_____

_____

2. Now come up with reasons **WHY you MUST** work out!

_____

_____

_____

3. Next, come up with your **PA's** and **EPA's** plan!

Remember, when making a goal you must be **SPECIFIC**. Cover the **5 W's** (who, what, when, where, and why) and you will succeed!

What: The PA's I will do three times a week are: (see PA list)

_____

_____

_____

When: _____

With Whom: _____

Where: _____

EPA's I will do daily are: (see list)

_____

_____

_____

Physical Actions and **Extra Physical Actions** are an important part to any health and fitness regime. Remember, it's all about "calories in- verses calories out!" Not only is it important to weight loss, it also helps you keep the weight off and will be a valuable **friend** throughout your life. Being physical helps prevent disease and improves your overall health. It helps your mind function better and your heart beat stronger! It doesn't matter what types of *physical actions* you perform – whether it be sports, yoga, walking, yard work or rollerblading, even walking up the stairs is beneficial.

Studies show that even as little as **thirty minutes** or more of **physical activity** per day can assist you in losing weight. Below is a list of **EXTRA P.A's** you can do daily to burn calories.

FYI: Drink at least eight 8 ounce glasses of water a day. Water is a natural appreciate suppressant, can help keep your stomach full and prevents dehydration. Like we've talked about in class, water is especially important when you work out!

EXTRA PHYSICAL ACTIONS LIST (EPA'S)

1. Walk up and down stairs.
2. Get up to change the channel.
3. Stand while playing with my game boy.
4. Park car farther away and walk.
5. Re-decorate your bedroom.
6. Get up for water during commercials.
7. Dance while folding laundry.
8. Walk during lunch break.
9. Take the long route to class.
10. Stand and stretch during computer breaks.
11. Stretch between classes.
12. Re-organize the kitchen cupboards.
13. Re-organize your closet.
14. Try on smaller size clothes.
15. Take the dog for a walk.
16. Pace while you're talking on the phone.
17. Hang upside down on your bed (okay not an exercise but great for getting blood to the brain!).

18. Deep breath, count to ten and exhale (do this five times).
19. Do twenty arm circles for no reason at all (your friends will wonder).
20. Do shoulder shrugs while you're waiting in line.
21. Volunteer to help with a car wash.
22. Play "Twister" or other indoor games that require movement.
23. Create a video of exercise routines with your friends.
24. Invite your friends over to dance.
25. Go for a bike ride.
26. Rake leaves.
27. Shovel snow.
28. Plant your own vegetables, fruits, or flowers.
29. Take a long walk or jog on the beach.

Physical Actions (Exercise)

PA's are activities you do **three times a week** or more for at least **20 minutes** like aerobics, treadmill, weights, step, jogging etc.

Here are some examples of PA's:

• Walking Briskly	• Tennis	• Running
• Bicycling	• Football	• Bicycling
• Dancing	• Baseball	• Soccer
• Swimming	• Volleyball	• Skating
• Jogging	• Trampoline	• Fitness classes
• Yoga	• Spin Class	

You get the idea, it's great if you can work up a sweat! By doing these kinds of activities you can really burn those calories and condition your heart and lungs, not to mention, clear your mind from the stresses of life! I promise you, you will be glad you did after!

"Only those who dare to fail greatly can ever achieve greatly."

- Robert F. Kennedy

CHAPTER 8

SUCCESS ACTION #4
INSPIRATION

A good support system is important to success in anything in life. We all need a little inspiration from time to time. A strong support team can help you get to your goal faster. Your support team can be anyone from a family member to a good friend, teacher, school counselor, your LHT coach, or online buddy. People who team up while on a weight loss plan are often much more successful than those who don't!

COMPLETING SUCCESS ACTION #3 WILL HELP YOU:
- Choose a weight loss buddy.
- Sign a Buddy Declaration.
- Learn how to inspire others.

"Alone we can do so little; together we can do so much."
- Helen Keller

FINDING AN INSPIRATIONAL BUDDY

Finding a weight loss buddy will help make the program more fun. What qualities make a good weight loss buddy?

Check the boxes you think are important to you in choosing a buddy.

❑ Has a similar goal.

❑ Will hold me accountable.

❑ Has a strong desire to succeed.

❑ Will support me unconditionally.

❑ Won't sabotage me.

❑ Is available to help me when I need them.

❑ Is someone I trust and look up to.

❑ Is committed to completing the LHT six week Action Plan with me no matter what!

Who do you know that has the qualifications you checked?

_____

Would they be interested in being your weight loss buddy?

_____

"The majority of the time, the thing that gets in the way of success is your brain."
- Chris Blake

BUDDY DECLARATION

We _____
commit to being buddies throughout the six week LHT Action Plan. We promise to:

❑ Check in with each other daily.

❑ Hold each other accountable to follow the LHT Action Plan and write in our journals daily.

❑ Do PA's together at least three times per week.

❑ Remind each other of our goals.

❑ Speak **action words** of encouragement, never discouragement.

❑ Celebrate even our small successes together.

❑ Be strong for each other when one of us is tempted.

❑ Support each other's decision to live a new, healthier lifestyle.

❑ Date:_____ Signed: _____

Signed: _____

ACTIONS OF A FRIEND

A Accepts you as you are

C Commits to hold you accountable

T Tells you the truth

I Inspires you to succeed

O Offers support

N Never judges

S Speaks words of affirmation

"People will forget what you said...they will forget what you did. But people will never forget...how you made them feel!"
- Maya Angelou

CHAPTER 9:
SUCCESS ACTION #5
AFFIRMATION

t's interesting to me how words that are spoken to us from the outside can hurt so much, yet what we don't often acknowledge is that the words we speak to ourselves daily, (internalization) often hurt us even more! Sadly, we cannot always control what others say to us, but we can control what we say to ourselves. **It is only when we change our INTERNAL conversation, that we can we have lasting life change**. This is a place where you will learn to change the words inside, and gain new **admiration** of the **POWER OF YOUR WORDS!**

Webster's dictionary defines an affirmation as:
Something declared to be true; a positive statement.

A statement asserting the existence or the truth of something.

There is great power in saying affirmations. They have the power to change both your self-perception, and your body-perception.

Remember the movie, "Field of Dreams", with Kevin Costner and the famous line, "If you build it, they will come?" Affirmations can be magical like that. "If you affirm them, they will come true!" Say one of these affirmations in the mirror out loud 10 times every morning!

I am totally fit and in control!

I am in charge of my emotions!

My body is beautiful!

I am totally in tune with my body!

I am already a success!

I am MY body's best friend!

I am an amazing person!

"It's not whether you get knocked down;
it's whether you get back up!"
- Vince Lombardi

"You've got to be very careful if you don't know
where you're going, because you might not get there."
- Yogi Berra

"No pressure, no diamonds."
- Mary Case

"A pessimist sees the difficulty in every opportunity;
an optimist sees the opportunity in every difficulty."
- Winston Churchill

You don't drown by falling in the water;
you drown by staying there."
- Edwin Louis Cole

38

CHAPTER 10:

SUCCESS ACTION #6
TEMPTATION

Life is full of temptations and frustrations, especially when you're trying to lose weight! I bet you think you're the only one who's had a hard time overcoming these emotions, but many other teens have had (or still have) the same challenge. You may not even realize that it may be emotions (not hunger) that may be responsible for sabotaging your weight loss.

COMPLETING SUCCESS ACTION #6 WILL TEACH YOU TO:

• Overcome temptations.
• Identify your own eating triggers.
• Correct emotional eating patterns.
• Learn why putting a band aid on an emotional wound doesn't work.

"Failure is the opportunity to begin again more intelligently."
- Henry Ford

EMOTIONAL EATING

Emotional eating is when you eat food because of emotions (feelings) instead of hunger. Almost everyone eats for emotional reasons once in a while. In fact, an estimated 75% of overeating is caused by emotions. That's a LOT of emotional eating!

When we're young we learn that food can bring us comfort, at least for the time we are eating it. Because of that, we often turn to food to heal our emotional needs. Emotional eating becomes a habit instead of learning how to resolve the real issues. I call this an emotional wound and overeating is an emotional bandage!

Feeling depressed, frustrated, lonely, angry, anxious, bored, or stressed can affect our self-perception and lead us to the cookie jar.

By figuring out what emotions cause you to overeat, we can learn to interrupt those behaviors and replace them with positive ones.

WHAT TRIGGERS YOU?
We eat for many reasons, other than hunger:

PRESSURIZATION: We often eat more when we're around others, like friends and family. It's our way of socializing and we feel left out if we don't join in. Friends and family can pressure us to eat (like grandma) without realizing what they're doing. If we say no, were afraid we might hurt their feelings, so we just go with the flow.

LOCATION: Who hasn't eaten something just because it was there? Like during the holidays when all those yummy treats are out in front of you ALL DAY LONG. How about staying at a friend's slumber party and they order PIZZA, and oh that smell! How can one resist those IN YOUR FACE temptations? You're not made of steel, right?!?

EMOTIONS: Why we eat in response to emotions is the million dollar question... and I've got some answers. Everyone has different emotional triggers, but these are some of the most common:

1. To stuff down (or avoid) a feeling or to try to fill a void, we may not even know we have. That void may be just needing a hug or some extra encouragement, or it can be as complex as missing a loved one or a deep fear of something.
2. We eat emotionally when we are bored, stressed, tired, depressed, angry or lonely, (which can happen often). We even eat when we're HAPPY, like at parties and celebrations!
3. We eat because we don't like ourselves, or don't feel we are worthy of some thing. Often overeating can be a form of self punishment.
   *See note on binge eating later in the book.

SO WHAT DO I DO WHEN I'M IN THESE SITUATIONS?

RECOGNITION is the key! To overcome any challenge you first have to RECOGNIZE it's a challenge! Once recognized, you can begin to find the solution.

HERE'S A SIMPLE WAY TO RECOGNIZE YOUR EMOTIONS IN ANY SITUATION.

IT'S CALLED THE H.A.L.T SYSTEM!

It's an old trick that works really well!

Whenever you notice yourself eating for emotional reasons, STOP and ask yourself, am I hungry, angry, lonely, or tired?

HUNGRY - ANGRY - LONELY - TIRED

H - A - L - T

If you don't know WHAT you're feeling, you can look at the emotions chart to help you figure it out. Then you can start learning how to deal with the real issue, instead of eating it!

ASSOCIATIONS: We associate activities with foods when we do something and eat at the same time. Our minds link up the two activities (like eating and watching T.V.), and then when we watch T.V our mind automatically reminds us, "Hey where's my Doritos?" A great example of this is going to the movies. What food do you automatically associate that with?

Can you think of other examples?
Do you eat while at the computer? How about in bed or while talking on the phone?

_____

_____

_____

_____

Journaling Your Emotions

To identify what emotions make you eat, you'll be keeping a record of feelings in your action planner. Write down how and what you're feeling when you eat for any other reason than hunger. You'll start to see a pattern and then you can go to work on the solution! By the way, don't be so hard on yourself when this happens. It's hard enough that you feel bad. You don't need to beat yourself up about it. **Guilt is against the rules on the LHT plan.**

GUILT: We believe that guilt, while on a weight loss program, serves no purpose. I mean, it doesn't help us feel better and it doesn't help us do better either, does it? Quite frankly, it usually makes us feel worse and cheat more, so what's the point? Decide when you go off-plan that you will be grown-up about it and learn from the experience and NOT FEEL GUILTY. Remember, the good news about eating healthy is that every meal is a new opportunity for a fresh start!

I'M NOT SURE WHAT I'M FEELING

There is a lot we can do to manage our feelings, but the first step is to recognize WHAT we are feeling.

Are You Stuffing Food or Stuffing Feelings? The following chart gives you an example by allowing you to identify what feelings you are really experiencing and what you can do to change it. It's important to recognize these feelings for what they really are so we aren't stuffing them down along with our food!

DO YOU SOMETIMES FEEL:	INSTEAD, WHAT IF YOU DECIDED TO FEEL?
Hurt	Compassion
Misunderstood, sad, betrayed, unappreciated, rejected	Be honest with yourself about why you are hurting. Ask yourself what about this situation hurt you, why it hurt, and how it made you feel. If you cannot tell the person that hurt you then write it in your journal or write them a letter. You don't even have to give it to them.
Lonely	Prayerful
Disconnected, missing friends, family, lost relationships, emptiness, hole in the middle	Many of us feel lonely even when we are surrounded by others. Look deep inside and ask yourself - what part of me feels lonely? What part of me feels empty? How can I fill that part up In a healthy way, other than with food? Can you ask for help or call a friend? If you don't feel like reaching out, then reach within and find faith in yourself.
Guilty	Decisive
Ashamed, worthless, failure, sinful, shameful	As I mentioned before, I am a firm believer that guilt around food serves no purpose. It doesn't help us feel better, eat less or even diet more the next day. It usually only makes us feel bad and eat more. Decide to leave no room in your life for guilt around food. DECIDE, "Okay I ate it, now what"? Take action and go back on the plan! It's as easy as that! Every meal you can make a new decision to start again. **NO MORE GUILT!**

Anger	Determination
Frustrated, resentful, out of control, mean, nasty, violent	Ask yourself, why am I really angry? Is it a disguise for another emotion I don't want to feel? Am I hurt or disappointed and turning to anger because it's an easier emotion to deal with? If I am truly angry I should express it in a constructive way, like talking to someone about it or writing it in my journal. I will turn my anger into determination and use its ENERGY to propel me forward, not backwards!
Fearful	Flexible
Embarrassed, ashamed, concerned, worried	Face your fears by being flexible and open to new things. What's the worst thing that could happen? I mean really ask yourself, If I do this what is the very worst thing that can happen? Now, face that fear and answer that for yourself: "Okay if that happens then I will _____?" (Die?) You're probably not going to die (though it may feel like it), and do you really think your worst fear is going to come true? Probably not. Sometimes the fear we feel is stronger than the reality of it happening! LHT believes that your FAITH should always be stronger than your FEAR!
Frustration	Action
Feeling out of control, not listened to, inadequate, unappreciated, overwhelmed	Appreciate the fact that FRUSTRATION often leads to ACTION! Most of the time we don't change until we are so frustrated we have no other choice. Make a list of items you feel frustrated about. Number them in order of importance. Start completing those that are most important and you will feel less frustrated because you'll be taking action!
Disappointed	Reflective
Sad, loss of hope, helpless, depressed, discouraged	Look inside to see why you are sad. Did someone let you down? Are you disappointed? Try forgiveness and realize we all make mistakes. The best way to help yourself when you are depressed is to take the focus off of yourself and help someone else! Deep depression can get worse when we are spending too much time alone and looking inward. As soon as you start giving and doing for others, your depression will get better.

USE THESE SELF REALZATION AFFIRMATIONS!

Positive Affirmation
I will take the time to understand the truth about why I am really hurting and what it means.

Positive Affirmation
I am never alone, because the LHT community is always with me!!!

Positive Affirmation
I have the power to control my next decision!

Positive Affirmation
I will be honest about whether I am truly angry or disguising it for another emotion.

Positive Affirmation
I will look at my fears in a constructive way and imagine the worst possible outcome. Then I will visualize how I would handle that outcome with success. I will live more in FAITH than in FEAR!

Positive Affirmation
I realize that frustration often leads to change and change is often good!

Positive Affirmation
I realize that in life disappointment can be sadness in disguise. I know that people can and will disappoint me in my life. I can either take it personally or choose not to. Sometimes people let us down without meaning to.

Positive Affirmation
I am healthy, active and alive!

Positive Affirmation
I can achieve anything I set my mind to!

Positive Affirmation
I am perfectly and wonderfully made!

"Don't forget to LOVE yourself."

CHAPTER 11:
WHAT IF FOOD IS CONTROLLING ME?

HELP... I CAN'T STOP EATING CARBS!

As a former binge eater myself, I struggle with loving carbohydrates, just like you do. I've tried a lot of things throughout my twenty-year career in the weight loss business and this is what I find works best. When someone is having a carbohydrate challenge, one of the quickest ways to get back on track is to "go off" carbohydrates for a day (you can have fruit and vegetables but no empty carbs). Taking a break allows you to get the carb taste out of your mind, (and mouth) and helps bring your insulin levels back into control. It also helps you lose excess water (which can make you feel heavier) and most importantly, helps you get back on track emotionally.

It's like if you had a toothache every day and just took some aspirin, instead of asking yourself, "WHAT is causing my toothache?" When you have food challenges, it's important to ask yourself, "WHY am I having these issues?" Make sure you are working on the wound (your emotions) and not just putting a bandage on it!

Being controlled by food in any way can be a very serious and dangerous problem, often requiring special attention. It's important that you know the warning signs so that you can recognize the signs if your weight issues are getting out of control. This is the only body you will ever have and certain conditions can be very, very dangerous to your long-term health.

"The greater the obstacle, the more glory in overcoming it."
- Moliere

"Kites rise highest against the wind—not with it."
- Winston Churchill

WHAT IS BULIMIA? Bulimia Nervosa is a serious eating disorder that can be fatal if left untreated. People who have bulimia nervosa routinely binge eat—consuming large amounts of food in a very short period of time, and immediately purge—ridding their bodies of the just-eaten food by self-inducing vomiting, taking enemas, or abusing laxatives or other medications. If left untreated, bulimia nervosa can lead to serious and even life-threatening problems, such as depression, anxiety disorders, heart damage, kidney damage, injury to all parts of the digestive system, and severe dental damage. Those with Bulimia Nervosa are at risk for dangerously impulsive, self-destructive behaviors, such as kleptomania, self-mutilation, alcohol and/or drug abuse, and sexual promiscuity. Bulimia Nervosa typically begins during adolescence, and while it most often occurs in women, it also affects men. Individuals with the disorder usually feel acutely out of control during both their bingeing and the purging episodes and afterwards suffer from intense feelings of shame, guilt, and self-loathing. Embarrassed by their behavior, they typically binge and purge in secret and are often successful in hiding their problem from others. If you or someone you know has this problem please tell your LHT Coach and ask them for a referral to someone who specializes in that area.

WHAT IS ANOREXIA? Anorexia is an extremely dangerous eating disorder in which a person intentionally deprives themselves of food and can literally starve to death in an attempt to be what they consider thin. The disorder involves extreme weight loss - at least 15% below the individual's healthy weight - and a refusal to maintain body weight that is even minimally normal for their age, height, and body frame. The disorder usually begins around the time of puberty and the onset is often associated with a stressful life event such as leaving home for college, or their parents divorcing. While more than 90% of the cases affect young women, the numbers of recognized cases of males with anorexia nervosa is increasing. Males can be a particular high risk for developing life-threatening medical problems as a direct result of the disorder, probably because they are too often diagnosed later than females. In their concerted efforts to continually reduce their weight, anorexics reduce their food and calorie intake through such rigid strategies as excluding what they perceive to be high fat or high calorie foods, limiting their food intake to just a few specific low calorie foods, bingeing and purging - purging after even the smallest meals, refusing to eat in public, and/or going to great lengths to avoid eating with even close friends or family. Anorexics become obsessed with food-hoarding, yet they will not allow themselves to eat any of it.

*As always, please check with your parents or physician before doing the LHT program.

46

CHAPTER 12:
SUCCESS ACTION #7
CLARIFICATION

CONGRATULATIONS!

It's time for some recognition of how much you have accomplished in just a few short weeks - time for reflection and appreciation of how true you've been to yourself (and your buddy if you had one).

COMPLETING SUCCESS ACTION #7 MEANS YOU WIN!!
- Let's review what you've learned.
- How many pounds and how much body fat did you lose?
- What's your new perception of yourself and of your body now?
- Let's plan the transition to make your knowledge and habits.
  part of your lifestyle by leaving you with new goals!

Wow, can you believe what you've done and accomplished in just six weeks? What you have **learned, dreamed and achieved?** You are truly amazing! We are so proud of you and all that you've accomplished. **YOU are a leader, an achiever, a motivator and a life changer!** Now, that you've successfully completed this part of the program, we hope that it encourages you to "**GO ON**" and continue all the new habits you've learned. We know it's not easy to make changes, it takes time, but with small steps you can achieve anything you set your mind to…we know you've learned that now!

You're a graduate and now a **forever part of the LHT family**, we hope you stay and become a mentor to others!

We hope you have some new **ACTION** words to use now like…**motivation inspiration, destination, participation, recreation, exploration and now anticipation of graduation!**

47

"Next Destination" Goal Setting Worksheet

It is important for me to set new goals for inspiration, so I can get to my next **destination.**

My new goals for the next six weeks are:

1. _____

2. _____

3. _____

4. _____

5. _____

6. _____

7. _____

Examples:

I will continue to increase my PA's and EPA's daily.

I will read a book of my choice about health and fitness.

I will become a LHT online mentor.

I will keep off the weight I lost.

I will continue to use the good eating habits I have learned.

Date: _____ Signed: _____

"The creation of a thousand forests is in one acorn!"
- Ralph Waldo Emerson

✂ cut here

Certificate of Completion

Diploma

This certifies that
the bearer

...as satisfactorily completed a Course of Study prescribed
by an accredited Institution of Learning

Cynthia Besson
- Founder -

Jimmy Badra
- Founder -

49

WHAT DOES BODY MASS INDEX MEAN?

The definition of overweight can mean different things to different people. For instance, a 5 foot 2 inch woman would be considered overweight at 165 pounds, while a 6 foot 2 inch man would be considered thin at 165 pounds.

How do you know what's the ideal weight for you? By creating the Body Mass Index they put everything on the same scale and adjusted for height. The BMI is used by doctors to assess whether someone is overweight or not. To determine IF and how much weight you need to lose, you'll need to know what your Body Mass Index (BMI) number is? A BMI of 25 to 30 is considered overweight. The good news is that even a small weight loss (just 10 percent of your current weight) will help to lower your risk of developing diseases associated with obesity.

Determining Your Body Mass Index (BMI)

To use the table below find the appropriate height (in inches) in the left-hand column. Move across the row to your current weight. The number at the top of the column is the BMI number for that height and weight.

BMI Chart

Weight (pounds)

Height (feet and inches)	100	110	120	130	140	150	160	170	180	190	200	210	220	230	240	250	260
4'6"	24	27	29	31	34	36	39	41	43	46	48	51	53	55	58	60	63
4'8"	22	25	27	29	31	34	36	38	40	43	45	48	49	52	54	56	58
4'10"	21	23	25	27	29	31	33	36	38	40	42	44	46	48	50	52	54
5'0"	20	21	23	25	27	29	31	33	35	38	39	41	43	45	47	49	51
5'2"	18	20	22	24	26	28	29	31	33	35	37	38	40	42	44	46	48
5'4"	17	19	21	22	24	26	27	29	31	33	34	36	38	39	41	43	45
5'6"	16	18	19	21	23	24	26	27	29	31	32	34	36	37	39	40	42
5'8"	15	17	18	20	21	23	24	26	27	29	30	32	33	35	36	38	40
5'10"	14	16	17	19	20	22	23	24	26	27	29	30	32	33	34	36	37
6'0"	14	15	16	18	19	20	22	23	24	26	27	28	30	31	33	34	35
6'2"	13	14	15	17	18	19	21	22	23	24	26	27	28	30	31	32	33
6'4"	12	13	15	16	17	18	19	21	22	23	24	26	27	28	29	30	32
6'6"	12	13	14	15	16	17	18	20	21	22	23	24	25	27	28	29	30
6'8"	11	12	13	14	15	16	18	19	20	21	22	23	24	25	26	27	29
6'10"	10	12	13	14	15	16	17	18	19	20	21	22	23	24	25	26	27
7'0"	10	11	12	13	14	15	16	17	18	19	20	21	22	23	24	25	26

Underweight   Normal Range   Overweight   Obese

How to use your ACTION Planner successfully

1. If you haven't already done so, please look at the graph on the previous page so you can see what your healthy weight range is.

2. Then, each time you eat something, write it in the blank area for that day so you'll have a record of what you ate. You can do this when you get home from school or at the end of each day. Place check marks in the boxes for each glass of water you drink.

3, Look at the food groups lists of proteins, fats, carbohydrates (carbs) dairy and fruits.

4. Try and pick something from the food groups that you like. For instance, in the dairy section if you don't like yogurt, have a slice of low-fat cheese for breakfast. Here is an example of how your plate should look when combine the proper food groups.

5. Don't forget to fill in your **Physical Actions** and your **Extra Physical Actions** each day.

6. Finally, write in your emotions each day so you'll be aware of what you're feeling. Also at the very bottom write what your self-perception is of your body that day? Are you saying mean things to yourself, or are you being kind? If you don't know what you're feeling, please look at the feelings graph on pages 42-43.

Here is a reminder of what each food group contains:

GRAINS
Any food made from wheat, rice, oats, cornmeal, barley or another cereal grain is a grain product. Bread, pasta, oatmeal, breakfast cereals, tortillas, and grits are examples of grain products.

VEGETABLES
Any vegetable or 100% vegetable juice counts as a member of the Vegetable Group. Vegetables may be raw or cooked; fresh, frozen, canned, or dried/dehydrated; and may be whole, cut-up, or mashed.

FRUITS
Any fruit or 100% fruit juice counts as part of the Fruit Group. Fruits may be fresh, canned, frozen, or dried, and may be whole, cut-up, or pureed.

DAIRY
All fluid milk products and many foods made from milk are considered part of this food group. Most Dairy Group choices should be fat-free or low-fat. Foods made from milk that retain their calcium content are part of the group. Foods made from milk that have little to no calcium, such as cream cheese, cream, and butter, are not. Calcium-fortified soymilk (soy beverage) is also part of the Dairy Group.

PROTEIN FOODS
All foods made from meat, poultry, seafood, beans and peas, eggs, processed soy products, nuts and seeds are considered part of the Protein Foods Group. Beans and peas are also part of the Vegetable Group.

FATS
Oils are fats that are liquid at room temperature, like Canola, Corn or Olive oil.

Solid fats are fats that are solid at room temperature, like butter and shortening. Solid fats come from many animal foods and can be made from vegetable oils through a process called hydrogenation. Some common fats you should be careful how much you eat are:

- Butter, stick margarine, milk fat, shortening, beef fat, pork fat, chicken fat, partially hydrogenated oil (read the label) mayonnaise and most salad dressings.

	BREAKFAST	LUNCH	DINNER
Sunday Water ☐☐☐☐☐☐			
Monday Water ☐☐☐☐☐☐			
Tuesday Water ☐☐☐☐☐☐			
Wednesday Water ☐☐☐☐☐☐			
Thursday Water ☐☐☐☐☐☐			
Friday Water ☐☐☐☐☐☐			
Saturday Water ☐☐☐☐☐☐			

PHYSICAL ACTIONS · EMOTIONS · PERCEPTIONS · WATER

EMOTIONS

PA & EPA

SNACKS

WORDS

PROTEIN · STARCH · FRUIT · VEGGIES · DAIRY · FAT · WATER

WORDS

	BREAKFAST	LUNCH	DINNER
Sunday Water ☐☐☐☐☐☐			
Monday Water ☐☐☐☐☐☐			
Tuesday Water ☐☐☐☐☐☐			
Wednesday Water ☐☐☐☐☐☐			
Thursday Water ☐☐☐☐☐☐			
Friday Water ☐☐☐☐☐☐			
Saturday Water ☐☐☐☐☐☐			

PHYSICAL ACTIONS · EMOTIONS · PERCEPTIONS · WATER
EMOTIONS
PA & EPA
SNACKS

PROTEIN · STARCH · FRUIT · VEGGIES · DAIRY · FAT · WATER

WORDS

	BREAKFAST	LUNCH	DINNER
Sunday Water ☐☐☐☐☐			
Monday Water ☐☐☐☐☐			
Tuesday Water ☐☐☐☐☐			
Wednesday Water ☐☐☐☐☐			
Thursday Water ☐☐☐☐☐			
Friday Water ☐☐☐☐☐			
Saturday Water ☐☐☐☐☐			

PHYSICAL ACTIONS · EMOTIONS · PERCEPTIONS · WATER

EMOTIONS

PA & EPA

SNACKS

WORDS

	BREAKFAST	LUNCH	DINNER
Sunday Water ☐☐☐☐☐☐☐☐			
Monday Water ☐☐☐☐☐☐☐☐			
Tuesday Water ☐☐☐☐☐☐☐☐			
Wednesday Water ☐☐☐☐☐☐☐☐			
Thursday Water ☐☐☐☐☐☐☐☐			
Friday Water ☐☐☐☐☐☐☐☐			
Saturday Water ☐☐☐☐☐☐☐☐			

PHYSICAL ACTIONS · EMOTIONS · PERCEPTIONS · WATER

EMOTIONS

PA & EPA

SNACKS

WORDS

WORDS

	BREAKFAST	LUNCH	DINNER
Sunday *Water* ☐☐☐☐☐☐☐☐			
Monday *Water* ☐☐☐☐☐☐☐☐			
Tuesday *Water* ☐☐☐☐☐☐☐☐			
Wednesday *Water* ☐☐☐☐☐☐☐☐			
Thursday *Water* ☐☐☐☐☐☐☐☐			
Friday *Water* ☐☐☐☐☐☐☐☐			
Saturday *Water* ☐☐☐☐☐☐☐☐			

PHYSICAL ACTIONS · EMOTIONS · PERCEPTIONS · WATER

SNACKS

PA & EPA

EMOTIONS

WORDS

PROTEIN · STARCH · FRUIT · VEGGIES · DAIRY · FAT · WATER

BREAKFAST **LUNCH** **DINNER**

WORDS

	BREAKFAST	LUNCH	DINNER
Sunday Water ☐☐☐☐☐			
Monday Water ☐☐☐☐☐			
Tuesday Water ☐☐☐☐☐			
Wednesday Water ☐☐☐☐☐			
Thursday Water ☐☐☐☐☐			
Friday Water ☐☐☐☐☐			
Saturday Water ☐☐☐☐☐			

EMOTIONS

PA & EPA

SNACKS

WORDS

PROTEIN · STARCH · FRUIT · VEGGIES · DAIRY · FAT · WATER

	BREAKFAST	LUNCH	DINNER
Sunday *Water* ☐☐☐☐☐			
Monday *Water* ☐☐☐☐☐			
Tuesday *Water* ☐☐☐☐☐			
Wednesday *Water* ☐☐☐☐☐			
Thursday *Water* ☐☐☐☐☐			
Friday *Water* ☐☐☐☐☐			
Saturday *Water* ☐☐☐☐☐			

PHYSICAL ACTIONS · EMOTIONS · PERCEPTIONS · WATER

EMOTIONS

PA & EPA

SNACKS

WORDS

... DAIRY · FAT · DINNER

PROTEIN · STARCH · FRUIT · VEGGIES
BREAKFAST · **LUNCH**

WORDS

	BREAKFAST	LUNCH	
Sunday Water ☐☐☐☐☐☐☐☐			
Monday Water ☐☐☐☐☐☐☐☐			
Tuesday Water ☐☐☐☐☐☐☐☐			
Wednesday Water ☐☐☐☐☐☐☐☐			
Thursday Water ☐☐☐☐☐☐☐☐			
Friday Water ☐☐☐☐☐☐☐☐			
Saturday Water ☐☐☐☐☐☐☐☐			

PHYSICAL ACTIONS · EMOTIONS · PERCEPTIONS · WATER

SNACKS

PA & EPA

EMOTIONS

WORDS

	BREAKFAST	LUNCH	DINNER
Sunday Water ☐☐☐☐☐☐☐☐			
Monday Water ☐☐☐☐☐☐☐☐			
Tuesday Water ☐☐☐☐☐☐☐☐			
Wednesday Water ☐☐☐☐☐☐☐☐			
Thursday Water ☐☐☐☐☐☐☐☐			
Friday Water ☐☐☐☐☐☐☐☐			
Saturday Water ☐☐☐☐☐☐☐☐			

PHYSICAL ACTIONS · EMOTIONS · PERCEPTIONS · WATER EMOTIONS

PA & EPA

SNACKS

WORDS

PROTEIN · STARCH · FRUIT · VEGGIES · DAIRY · FAT · WATER

	BREAKFAST	LUNCH	DINNER
Sunday Water ☐☐☐☐☐☐☐☐			
Monday Water ☐☐☐☐☐☐☐☐			
Tuesday Water ☐☐☐☐☐☐☐☐			
Wednesday Water ☐☐☐☐☐☐☐☐			
Thursday Water ☐☐☐☐☐☐☐☐			
Friday Water ☐☐☐☐☐☐☐☐			
Saturday Water ☐☐☐☐☐☐☐☐			

PHYSICAL ACTIONS · EMOTIONS · PERCEPTIONS · WATER
SNACKS　　**PA & EPA**　　**EMOTIONS**

WORDS
